TIGER MOTH

The Fortune Cookies of Weevil

by Aaron Reynolds

illustrated by Erik Lervold

Cast of characters

Kung Pow

Tiger Moth

The next day. Lunch was the typical leftover slop.

The Dragonfly boys were taking up the table across the canteen, with Dragon dead centre in the swarm. They were flicking slime balls at kids going by.

When suddenly, special delivery showed up.

Look at that.

It's a delivery boy from StarBugs.

Yup.

The delivery boy took his precious bundle and headed straight for Dragon.

First the Fruit Fly boys.

Now Dragon?

Time to stick our noses where they don't belong.

I'll do it.

Are you sure?

Sneak and peek. I've got it.

All right. Just listen in. Find out what's going on.

Okay.

And remember. Blend in.

Okay!

Trip!

BAM!

Hey, watch it, maggot!

Dragon was a head and feelers taller than Kung Pow.

I would've jumped in, but there comes a time in every apprentice's life when they have to fly on their own, or get swatted trying.

Maybe I should teach you some manners, bug!

Yeah? Well, you are!

"You are?!" Hahaha. Good one! Come on, boys.

So much for flying on his own.

"You are?"

Leave me alone!

I won't say another word.

Maybe this wasn't a complete failure. Fortune cookie at ten o'clock.

Kung, you may have no style, but you get the job done.

What's it say?

TINK!

TINK!

TINK!

The Tsetses stumbled right into our little trap.

Ugh! These are brand new shoes.

That took the air out of their walk real fast.

Later that day at my house . . .

My mind had been racing faster than a wasp in a windsock. It was time to put my plan into place.

What's the plan, Tiger?

A new message from "W". I had these made.

Wednesday's meeting cancelled. Wait for instructions.

W

It was Wednesday night. We were fashionably early for the little shindig with "W".

SLUGS

The back room of the StarBugs shop was loaded to the rafters with boxes and boxes of fortune cookies.

And the message is . . .

krack!

My criminal friends! No doubt you have heard of my work. Join with me and the rewards will be rich. I await your reply.

~Weevil

27

Then Kung Pow started to back up and . . .

Bump!

CRASH!

Ooops. Sorry.

Kung, you're so clumsy.

Isn't it great?

Hmmm. I like your style.

With the fortune cookies crumbled, we turned off the lights and waited for the guest of honour.

mWaa-Ha!
mWaa-Ha!
mWaa-Ha!
mWaaa-Ha-Ha!!!
mWaaa-Ha-Ha!!
mWaa-Ha!

That's taking it a little far, don't you think?

Too over the top?

Just a bit.

Okay.

And you're wrong, Weevil. This stops here. Tonight!

Who will stop me? A little butterfly and his *cockroach* friend?

I'm no butterfly. I am Tiger Moth, Insect Ninja!

That's woodlouse. Woodlouse!

Get him!

Get him?

3

Yup. He got away. Didn't see that one coming.

It wasn't a complete loss. We crushed all the cookies, stopping him from kicking his crime spree into high gear.

And we kept Dragon, the Fruit Flies, and the Tsetses from getting into any more trouble.

100% pure Weevil.

But one thing was clear. There was a new bad guy in town. And his name was Weevil.

ABOUT THE AUTHOR

Aaron Reynolds loves insects and loves books, so Tiger Moth was a perfect blend of both. Aaron is the author of several great books for children, including *Chicks and Salsa*, which *Publishers Weekly* called "a literary fandango" that "even confirmed macaroni-and-cheese lovers will devour." Aaron had no idea what a "fandango" was, but after looking it up in the dictionary (it means "playful and silly behaviour"), he hopes to write several more fandangos in the future. He lives with his wife, two children, and four insect-obsessed cats.

ABOUT THE ILLUSTRATOR

Erik Lervold was born in Puerto Rico, a small island in the Caribbean, and has been a professional painter. He attended the University of Puerto Rico's Mayaguez campus, where he studied Civil Engineering. Deciding that he wanted to be a full-time artist, he attended the Minneapolis College of Art and Design, studied Comic Art, and graduated in 2004. Erik teaches classes in libraries and has taught art in the Minnesota Children's Museum. He loves the colour green and has a collectiom of really big goggles. He also loves sandwiches. If you want him to be your friend, bring him a roast beef sandwich and he will love you forever.

GLOSSARY

apprentice one who learns from someone else, just as Kung Pow learns to be a ninja from Tiger Moth

beeswax slang word for "business" as in "That's my personal beeswax!"

buffet big meal where people serve themselves

dojo school or practice area where people and insects can learn martial arts, like karate or judo

fortune something that might happen to you in the future

maggot early stage of an insect. If you find a maggot at a buffet, don't stay for dessert!

shindig party

spree uncontrolled, energetic activity. Crooks go on crime sprees. Sharks go on eating sprees.

tsetse kind of African fly; some tsetse flies carry a form of sleeping sickness

FROM THE NINJA NOTEBOOK

Secret messages

History is full of stories of people sending secret messages to other people. Two thousand years ago, the ancient Greeks used invisible ink to send messages between armies. They made the ink from the clear juice of plants or nuts. When the message was heated over a flame, the ink turned dark and could then be read.

During World War II, a German spy used a jumper to send a secret message. When the jumper was unravelled, the knots in the wool stood for letters of the alphabet. The wool could be held up against an alphabet printed on a wall, and the spy's companions could work out the secret message.

Secret messages have also been hidden inside special containers. Hollow spaces for messages have been made inside books, shoes, pens, cameras, and even food!

During the 1970s, US spies used a special container made out of the two halves of a silver coin. The fake coin could hold a tiny dot of film with a message printed on it. A spy could simply press one side of it and the coin would open.

Sometimes spies would leave messages for each other. They would have a special place to leave them, where no one else would think of looking. The special place, or "drop point", might be a hollow brick inside a wall, a hole in a tree, or even the cistern of a restaurant's toilet. Hmmm.

DISCUSSION QUESTIONS

1. Do you think Weevil's idea to send secret messages through fortune cookies was a good plan? Do you have a better way to send secret messages to your friends?

2. Why did Tiger Moth tell Kung Pow on page 23, "We'll work on your disguises later"?

3. Tiger Moth and Kung Pow destroy all the fortune cookies they find in Weevil's storage room. The cookies didn't belong to them. Do you think it was okay for them to destroy someone else's property? Why or why not? Would it be okay to do that in real life?

100% pure Weevil.

WRITING PROMPTS

1. Weevil escapes at the end of the story by using a smoke bomb. It looks like Weevil was prepared in case anyone tried to stop him. Tiger Moth and Kung Pow should have been better prepared, too. Write down your own ideas about how they could have stopped Weevil.

2. Do you think Weevil will come back and cause more problems for Tiger Moth? Describe what you think Weevil's next evil plan will be. Will Tiger and Kung Pow be able to stop him again?

3. Some people believe the fortunes they get from fortune cookies. Imagine that you just bought a fortune cookie from StarBugs. What does your fortune say? Write down what it is. Does it come true?

More amazing adventures!

When Zack Allen is bullied at school, he invents a robot super suit to help him fight evil in the playground and beyond. He becomes Zinc Alloy, the world's newest superhero!